DRAGONS, GIANTS & WITCHES

CHRISTOPHER RAWSON

Illustrated by
STEPHEN CARTWRIGHT

CONTENTS

Consultant: Eric Maple

Reading Expert: Betty Root
Centre for the Teaching of Reading
University of Reading

Long Ago

Long ago, people went on journeys to far-away lands. They came home with stories of the monsters they had seen with wings and long tails.

Some had scales on their bodies, like fish, and rows of sharp teeth. Some even puffed out fire and smoke. People called them dragons.

Some dragons lived in caves. They guarded the treasure they had stolen from rich travellers.

Some lived up in the sky. When there was a storm, people said it was because the sky dragon was angry.

Others lived at the bottom of the sea. Sometimes they came up and frightened sailors.

Most dragons were kind and friendly.

But some were fierce and not friendly at all.

All dragons were large and needed a lot to eat.

Some people blamed dragons for everything. They even believed that lightning was a jet of flame from a dragon's mouth.

Sometimes dragons had terrible fights. They hissed and roared and tried to kill each other. Everyone came to watch and cheer.

Beware of Dragons

People always stayed as far away from dragons as they could. But if a fierce dragon flew down, brave soldiers in armour came out to fight it.

When people travelled through a country where there were dragons, they avoided big caves, deep holes and dark woods where they might live.

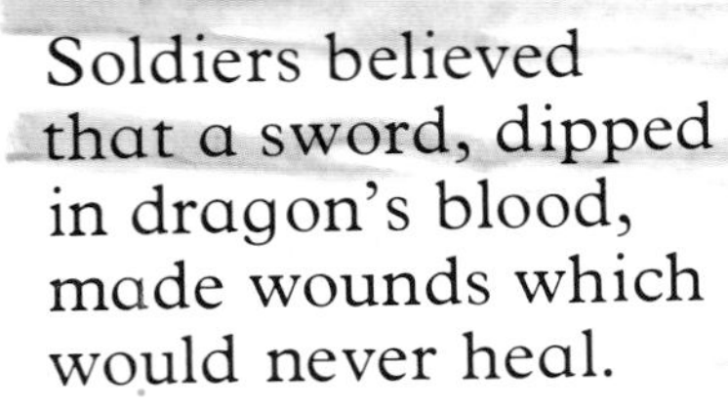

Soldiers believed that a sword, dipped in dragon's blood, made wounds which would never heal.

A dragon's breath was poisonous. Just one puff could kill a soldier.

A bath in dragon's blood helped people see into the future.

A dragon's tooth used to bring good luck.

People believed that dragon fat made good eye ointment.

Some people even said
that if dragon's teeth were
sown in the ground, they would
grow into fighting soldiers.

Some dragon slayers kept the heads
and tails of dragons they had killed
to show how brave they had been.

The Cock and Dragon

Long ago and far away in China, all cocks had big horns on their heads. Of course, they had bright red combs as well, just as cocks have today.

One day a huge dragon came flying out of the clouds. He did not look fierce like most dragons. He looked sad and cried big dragon tears.

Just then a cock walked by. "Hello," he said. "What is the matter with you?" The dragon sniffed. "I want to fly to Heaven. I have fine wings."

"But I have no horns," he said. "I am afraid the Heavenly People will laugh at me. Please will you lend me your horns?"

The cock scratched his head.
He thought, if I lend my horns to the dragon, will he give them back? He asked his friend, the worm.

"My good friend," said the worm, "I am sure the dragon will bring them back." So the cock gave his horns to the dragon, who flew away.

The cock waited and waited for the dragon. But he never came back. So the cock ate the worm, and cocks have eaten worms ever since.

Now, every morning at dawn, all cocks look up and cry "Cock-a-doodle-doo". In cock language, this means "Dragon, where are my horns?"

Victor of Lucerne

Many years ago there was a barrel maker called Victor. He lived beside a lake in a town called Lucerne in the middle of Switzerland.

One day he set out to explore the woods on Mount Pilatus. He wanted to choose the very best trees to make some new barrels.

Victor walked all day in the woods. He looked for the trees that were tall and straight. He marked each one with a piece of chalk.

Because he was looking up at the trees he did not see a big hole in the ground. "Help!" he cried, as he fell down it. But no one heard him.

Down and down he went, turning over and over in the air. At last, he landed with a splosh in the middle of a pool of mud at the bottom.

There he lay in the mud all night. Next morning, Victor stood up and looked round. He was at the bottom of a huge hole with steep sides.

Victor tried to climb. "I'll soon get out of here," he thought.

But every time he got a little way up, he slipped down to the bottom again.

Victor tried all morning. Then he just sat down and began to cry.

Suddenly there was a rumbling noise. Victor turned round and saw two huge dragons coming out of the cave.

The dragons had big bright eyes and shiny teeth. They blinked at Victor and licked their lips.

Poor Victor was very frightened.
He wanted to run away. But there was nowhere to go. "Don't eat me," he cried. "I won't do you any harm."

But the dragons just smiled at him and were not fierce at all.
They seemed quite pleased to have a new friend in their cave.

Soon they curled up on the floor of the cave and went to sleep.
"It might not be so bad down here after all," thought Victor.

But after a few days he was bored. The dragons just wanted to sleep all the time. There was nothing for Victor to do and no one to talk to.

All through the winter Victor lived in the hole. There was only grass to eat and drips of water to drink. Victor grew thinner and thinner.

Then, one day, it was Spring. One dragon woke up and yawned. It gave a great roar, flapped its wings and flew up out of the hole.

"Oh no!" said Victor. "If the other dragon flies away, I will never get out of here." So he held on to its tail as hard as he could.

Up and up they went, out of the hole and up into the sky. They flew over the trees until they landed right on the top of Mount Pilatus.

Victor walked all day and, at last, he reached Lucerne. The people cheered when they saw him. They thought he had died on the mountain.

Victor was very hungry after eating only grass for six months. He had a huge feast. He ate and ate for three whole days.

But Victor ate too much. He went to bed with a terrible pain in his tummy. The doctor came and gave him some medicine. But, after two days, he died.

All Victor's money was given to the Church. The people were so sad that he had died. They made a statue of him so they would not forget him.

The Lambton Worm

Lord Lambton was a kind old man who lived in Lambton Hall in England. The River Wear flowed deep and wide past the front of his house.

The old Lord's son was a lazy lad. He would not go to church on Sunday mornings. Instead he went fishing in the River Wear.

One Sunday, he fished all morning but did not catch anything. There were no fish, not even tiddlers.

Young Lambton grew crosser and crosser. He shouted, cried and jumped up and down.

Suddenly there was a tug on the line. "A fish at last," he thought. "I hope it's a big one."

But when he pulled it out of the river, it was not a fish at all. It was pink and slippery. It was an enormous worm.

Just then an old man walked by. "That worm will make trouble," he said. "But you must keep it. Don't put it back in the river."

The old man went away. Young Lambton wondered what to do with the enormous worm.

He pulled the hook from its mouth. Then he picked it up and pushed it down the well.

But one day the worm crawled out.

It had grown even more enormous.

It slithered down the hill,
over the bank and into the river.
It curled itself round a big rock
and lay there, fast asleep.

Sometimes it came out of the river.
It chased the cows all round the
fields, and frightened the people
who lived in the village.

Young Lambton did not know what to do.
He thought the terrible worm was all his fault.

He said goodbye to his father. Then he set out for the Holy Land to ask God to forgive him.

There he knelt every day and prayed that the worm would go away and trouble his father no more.

But the worm did not go away.
Soon the people hardly dared to go out of their houses. So they fed it with milk to keep it happy.

Every day they filled a huge trough right to the top with milk.
Every day the worm came and drank until the trough was empty.

But sometimes the people were too frightened to feed the Lambton worm. Then it hissed and roared at them.

It wrapped its tail round the biggest trees in the park. Then it pulled until they came out of the ground.

For seven years many brave knights came to fight the worm. But the worm was always too strong for them.

It lashed with its tail.
Then it squeezed and squirmed until no one would fight any more.

The old Lord was happy when at last young Lambton came home. But he looked even more frightened than before.

The old man said "Go and talk to the wise woman of Brugeford. She will tell you how to kill the worm."

The old woman said, "No one else but you can kill the worm. But you must go to the blacksmith who will make you a special suit of armour."

The blacksmith hammered red hot iron into sharp and shining spikes.
Then he fixed the spikes, one by one, all over young Lambton's armour.

Young Lambton put on his armour and sword.

He prayed all night for strength to kill the worm.

As the sun came up, he waited for battle.

When the worm saw young Lambton,
it wrapped itself round him,
and squeezed with all its strength.
But the spikes were terribly sharp.

Every time the worm squeezed, the spikes stuck further and further in to it. At last, it gave a cry of pain and unwound its slimy body.

Now young Lambton had his chance. Lifting his sword above his head, he aimed a mighty blow at the worm, and chopped it clean in half.

The beast was dead at last. The head and the body were washed away by the river and never seen again. And that was the end of the Lambton Worm.

Stan Bolovan and the Dragon

Stan Bolovan was a poor woodcutter. He lived in the forest with his wife. They were very happy but for one thing. They had no children.

One day in the forest, Stan met a wizard who gave him one wish. Stan said "I wish for as many children as my wife is thinking about now."

When Stan arrived home, his wife had not one . . .

not ten or twenty, or even fifty . . .

but a hundred children. "Oh no," groaned Stan.

They ate such a lot, Stan could not feed them all. One day he set out to make his fortune.

Soon he met a shepherd who promised him some sheep. But first he had to get rid of a dragon.

Bravely, Stan went up to the dragon. "I bet I can squeeze a stone until the water runs out," he said.

"Bet you can't," said the dragon. Stan took a lump of cheese from his bag. It looked just like a stone. He squeezed until water ran out.

"Now watch me," said the dragon. He picked up a huge rock and squeezed and squeezed. But he could not make one drop of water run out.

The dragon was very frightened. He thought Stan must be the strongest man in the world. "I will give you another chance," said Stan.

"If you can beat me this time," said the dragon, "I promise to give you half my treasure." So they set off towards the dragon's cave.

The dragon's old mother lived in the cave. "What shall we do?" asked the dragon. And he told her how Stan could squeeze water from rocks.

"I bet you can throw your club further than Stan can," she said. Stan trembled with fear when he saw the dragon's big, heavy club.

The dragon picked up his club. With a huge grunt, he threw the club over the mountain. "Oh dear," thought Stan, "I will never beat that."

Then he had a good idea. "Wait," he shouted to the dragon. "I cannot throw yet. The moon will get in the way."

The dragon stopped and stared at Stan.

He was so frightened, he trembled and shook.

Then he ran back to his cave, crying all the way.

That night Stan heard the dragons whispering. They were planning to kill him when he was asleep.

When Stan went to bed, he put a log under the bedclothes. Then he hid under the bed and waited.

In the middle of the night, the dragon crept in with his club.

He hit the log just where Stan's head should have been.

When the dragon told his mother, she laughed.

She jumped up and down.

"Well done," she cried. "That has got rid of him."

At that moment, Stan walked in., "Good morning," he said, "I hope you both slept well."

"I seem to have a little bump on my head today. I think a flea must have bitten me in the night."

The two dragons got a terrible shock. They were quite sure that Stan was dead in his bed.

They got out their sacks of money and treasures. "Take it all." they cried, "Go away. Leave us alone."

"If you want me to go," said Stan, "you must carry it for me." Sadly the dragon picked up his treasure and followed Stan home.

When the dragon saw all the children, he was terrified. He dropped the treasure and ran away. Stan and his family were never hungry again.

Famous Dragon Slayers

Once long ago, there was a young Christian knight called George. One day he was riding past a lake where a fierce dragon lived.

George killed the dragon and saved the King's daughter. The King and all his people became Christians, and the knight became Saint George.

King Cracus of Poland once tricked a very dangerous dragon. He poisoned it by putting pitch and sulphur in its food when it was not looking.

Another famous dragon fighter made a shield of mirror glass. The dragon got such a fright when it saw its own face, it rolled over and died.

Who kills the Dragon?

This is the maze of King Zoz. He keeps a fierce dragon called Ug in a cave in the middle. The King has promised that his daughter shall marry the knight who kills the dragon.

There is only one way in. Which knight gets into the cave?

Red Beard draws his sword. He is ready to find his way into the maze.

DANGER
NO ENTRY
Black Beard is armed with a mighty club. Can he find his way to the dragon's cave?
White Beard has sharpened his spear. Perhaps he will be the lucky one.

Find the Dragon's Treasure

Here is a plan of the rooms in the dragon's cellar. They are all empty except one which is full of treasure. The dragon has promised to share it with the giant if he can find it.

But the dragon has made some rules. The giant must begin at START and end at FINISH. And he may only go through each room once, either on the way to the treasure or on the way back.

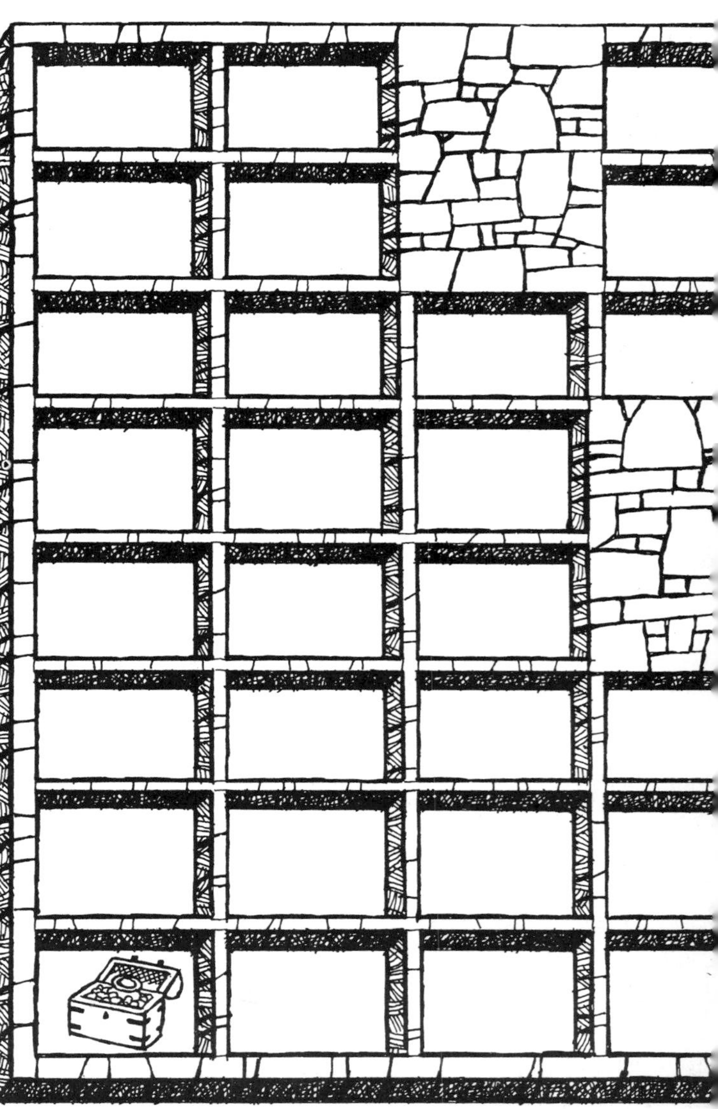

ılso he may only go from room to
oom either up and down or across
ut not diagonally. See if you can
vork out how the giant gets the
reasure. The answer is on page 96

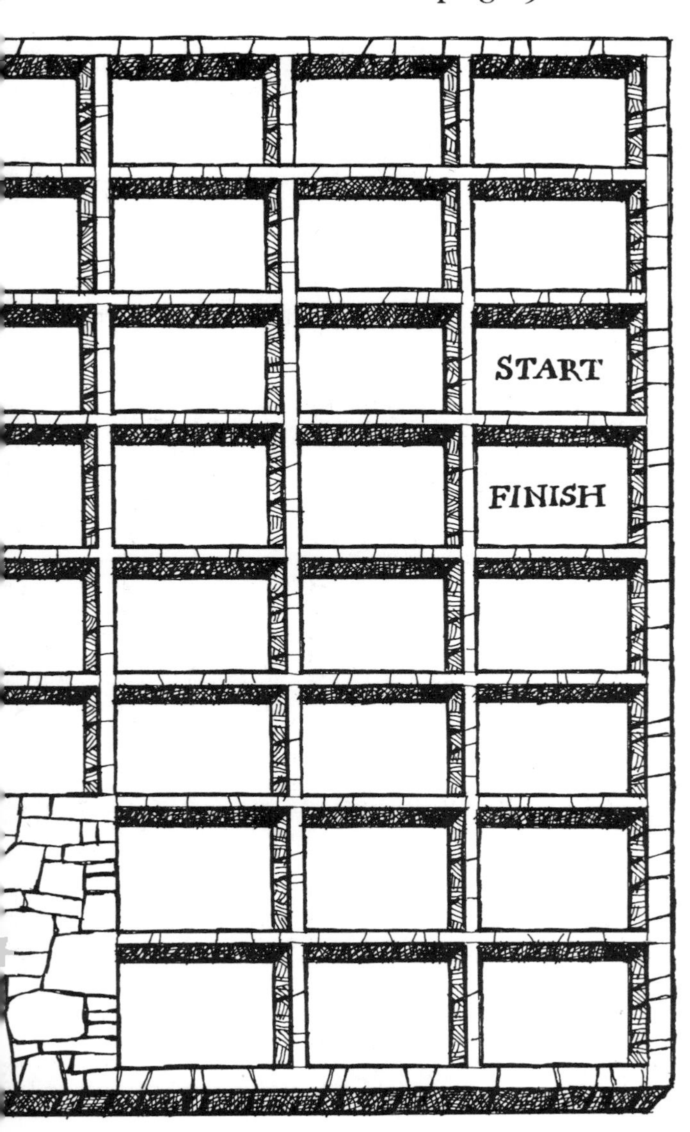

All sorts of Giants

There are lots and lots of stories about giants—good giants, bad giants, middle-sized giants and giant giants.

This really big giant tried to hit people with his club. But he was so slow he always missed them.

These two giants liked fighting. They shouted and roared but neither of them won the battles.

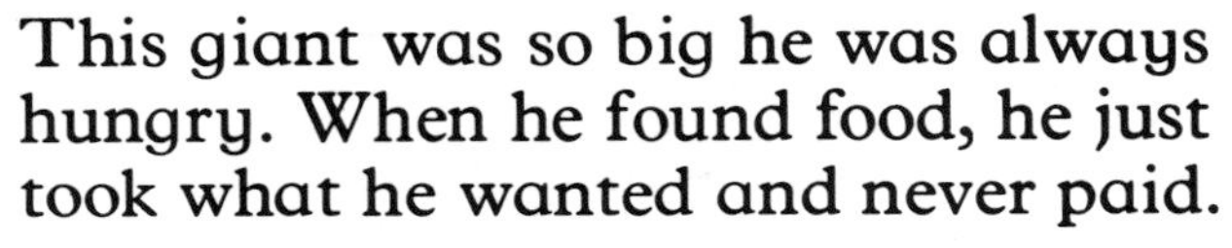

This giant was so big he was always hungry. When he found food, he just took what he wanted and never paid.

A mountain giant lived all alone in a cave. He liked hiding behind rocks and playing tricks on travellers.

This stupid giant sat down, even on someone's house, when he was tired.

A very sad giant cried all day and his tears made a great lake.

This was a kind giant who was friendly and helpful to grannies.

The Giant of St Michael's Mount

The giant who lived on St Michael's Mount and the giant who lived on Trecrobben Hill were shoe makers. But they only had one hammer.

One day the giant on St Michael's Mount shouted to his friend, "Hello, giant Trecrobben. Please will you lend me the hammer?"

Giant Trecrobben picked it up and threw it over the water. “Look out!” he shouted, “here it comes.”

The wife of the giant on St Michael’s Mount was in her cave. She ran out when she heard the shouting.

But she did not see the hammer. It landed on the top of her head and she fell down and died.

The two giants were so sad they could not think what to do. They sat down and cried so much, they made a great storm of giant tears.

Some people say they lifted up the church and buried the giant’s wife under it. Others say they just rolled her down the hill into the sea.

Heimo, the big bad Giant

Once there was a bad giant called Heimo. He ruled over all the lands in Austria beside the River Inn.

When Heimo was angry, he ran through the villages, knocking down the houses and frightening all the people.

Then one day God spoke to Heimo. He told him to stop being a nuisance.

So Heimo became a monk and started to build a monastery.

The devil was cross that God had turned Heimo into a good giant. He sent a dragon to frighten him and stop him building his monastery.

But Heimo knew God would protect him. So he went out all alone to fight the dragon. He cut out its tongue which was longer than a bed.

Then Heimo finished building his monastery. He lived there for many years, helping the poor people and looking after their children.

When Heimo died they put his body in a coffin long enough for ten men. Then they built a statue of him, holding up the dragon's tongue.

Patrick O'Brien, the Irish Giant

This is the story of Patrick O'Brien. He built houses in Ireland about 150 years ago.

Patrick was nearly three metres tall. People used to pay lots of money just to come and look at him.

But Patrick did not get any money. He was put in prison because he could not pay for his food.

When he was let out, he went to London. Everyone wanted to meet the friendly Irish giant and he soon became rich and famous.

He used to walk round the streets of London in the middle of the night. People ran away when he stopped to light his pipe from a gas lamp.

Patrick was so tall that a special coach was made for him to ride in. A big box was fixed under the floor to make enough room for his legs.

One day, a highwayman tried to rob Patrick's coach. But when Patrick leaned out of the window, the robber was so frightened he galloped away.

When he was at home he sat on the table. There were no chairs big enough for Patrick to sit on.

But poor Patrick was not very strong. Sometimes he needed help to climb up steep hills.

When he died, his skeleton was preserved. You can see it at the Royal College of Surgeons in London.

Jon and the Troll wife

There was once a poor farmer who lived far away in the north of the world. The farmer's wife was dead and he had one son called Jon.

All through the spring and summer, they worked in the fields. But in the autumn they travelled far beyond the mountains to fish in the sea.

One year the farmer said to Jon, "You must go alone. I am too old now. But remember to hurry past the big black rock where the trolls live."

When Jon was in the mountains, there was a storm. The thunder boomed and the lightning flashed. Suddenly Jon saw a big black rock.

He was so pleased to see a place to shelter, he forgot his father's warning. He drove his horses under the rock and let them eat the grass.

He unpacked his basket of food and sat down outside the cave to eat his supper. He had some cheese, a loaf of bread, an apple and one big fish.

Suddenly from inside the cave, he heard two babies crying, "We want food, we are so hungry."

Jon picked up the fish. He cut it in half, and spread the two halves with butter.

Then he threw them into the cave. "Here you are," he shouted. At once the crying stopped.

Jon was tired and lay down. He was just going to sleep when he saw a huge troll wife going into the cave. "I smell a man," she growled.

But when the troll wife came out, she gave Jon a big smile. "Thank you for feeding my children," she said, carrying him into the cave.

Inside the cave, the troll wife picked up her children. "You shall sleep in their bed," she said to Jon. Soon he was fast asleep.

Next morning she gave Jon fried fish for breakfast and he told her all about his old father. The troll wife gave Jon some magic fishing hooks.

Before Jon left, the troll wife said "When you get to the seashore, tie up your horses on the beach. I will look after them all through the winter."

"You must find the old man who lives in the tumbledown hut. Use the magic hooks, and only go fishing near the pointed rock."

When Jon reached the seashore, the fishermen laughed at him. "Who will look after your horses?" they asked. Jon said nothing about the troll wife.

Then he went to look for the old man who had a boat. "You won't catch any fish with me," the old man said, "I never have any luck."

Next morning Jon looked at the old man's boat. It was full of holes. The old man looked very sad. "We can't go fishing today," he said.

"I'll soon mend it," said Jon. He got some tar and pieces of wood, and patched up all the holes. Soon the boat was as good as new.

When they rowed near the pointed rock, Jon remembered the magic hooks that the troll wife had given him. "Let's try fishing with these," he said.

First they tied the hooks to their lines. Then they put worms on the hooks. As soon as the hooks were in the water, the fish began to bite.

On the first day, they filled their boat three times. Each time they took the fish back to the shore, cleaned them and hung them up to dry.

When the other fishermen saw all Jon's fish, they were amazed. "Where did you get them all?" they asked. So Jon told them where to fish.

Next day they all tried fishing there, but they caught nothing. Only Jon and the old man caught more and more fish on their magic hooks.

Then on the last day of winter, they both felt big tugs on their lines. When they pulled their lines up, the magic hooks had disappeared.

Now it was time for Jon to take his share of the fish home to his father. When he went to fetch his horses, he found a big brown horse there too.

Jon loaded all the fish on to the big brown horse. When he reached the troll's cave, he gave half of his fish to the friendly old troll wife.

She thanked Jon and said to him, "One day you will have a dream about me. Then you must come back to this cave. Everything here will be yours."

Jon rode back to his father. After a year, he had a dream about the troll wife. He told his father he was going on a secret journey.

When Jon got to the cave, he called "Hello, troll wife. Are you there?" But no one answered.

Inside the cave, he found two big boxes. Each one had his name written on it.

Suddenly he heard a noise outside the cave. It was the big brown horse which had carried all the fish.

Jon tied the boxes on the horse's back. Then he led it carefully over the mountains, back to where his father was waiting.

The boxes were full of troll treasure and gold. The kind old troll wife had never forgotten how one day long ago Jon had fed her hungry babies.

Niels and the Giants

A man and his wife once lived in a tiny cottage right on the top of a high and windy hill.

They had two sons. The older one, called Rasmus, helped his father mind the sheep all day.

The younger son, called Niels, never helped at all. He just liked to go out shooting.

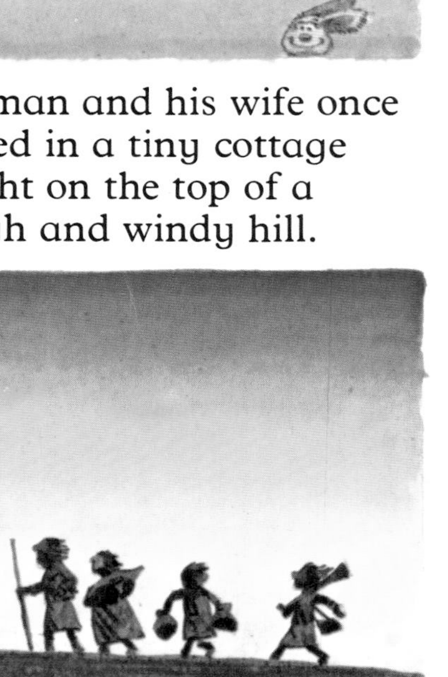

The shepherd's wife had always wanted to see the Pope. One day they set off to travel to Rome.

On the first evening, they came to a cross-roads. As they were very tired, they stopped to rest.

Father, mother and Rasmus lay down to sleep.
But Niels climbed a tall tree to keep guard.

After a while, Niels saw three giants come into a clearing in the forest. They made a fire and sat on the ground to eat huge chunks of meat.

The giants were so big that their spoons were like spades, and their forks were as big as hay forks. Niels decided to play a trick on them.

He fired his gun at one of the giant's forks, just as the giant was about to eat a piece of meat. Niels thought they could not see him.

The bullet hit the fork, and the fork stuck into the giant's chin. "Ow!" shouted the giant. He looked up and saw Niels sitting in the tree.

Before Niels had time to run away, the giant came crashing through the trees. "Any more tricks from you," he said, "and I'll stamp you into the ground!"

"But you're just the boy we need to defeat our enemy, the King. You can go into the castle and help us to capture his daughter, the princess."

"Every time we try to climb the high castle walls, the King's dog begins to bark. Then all the King's soldiers wake up again."

"Yes," boomed another giant. "We have cast a spell on the castle to send everyone to sleep. But the spell won't work on the King's dog."

When they arrived at the castle, Niels said "But I can't climb up there." "Oh yes you can!" said the giant. "I'm going to throw you up."

Niels landed with a bump on the top of the wall. He looked down at the giants. "Hurry up!" they shouted. "Shoot the dog and let us in."

Niels decided not to help the giants. He did not want to shoot the dog, which was nice and friendly. So he just gave it a pat to stop it barking.

Niels peeped into the first room. He saw a huge sword hanging on the wall. Beside the sword was a golden cup with words round the top.

The words on the cup said: WHOEVER DRINKS THIS WINE MAY USE THIS SWORD TO SAVE THE PRINCESS.

Niels read the words. Then he picked up the golden cup. He drank a little of the wine.

Then he tried to lift the sword. He pulled with all his might. But the sword would not move.

Niels peeped into another room. He found the beautiful princess asleep in bed.

"The giants must never capture her," he thought. So he ran back and drank all the rest of the wine.

With one mighty heave, he pulled out the sword. "Now I'll go and see the giants," he said.

The castle had two doors. One was very big and the other was very small. Niels could hear the giants shouting outside, "Let us in, let us in."

When Niels saw the two doors, he had an idea. "I can't open the big door," he shouted. "You'll have to come in through the small one."

Niels opened the small door. Then he hid round the corner, out of sight. As each giant bent down to come in, he chopped off his head with one blow.

"Hooray!" shouted Niels. "I've saved the princess." Then he began to wonder if the King would be cross with him for using the magic sword.

He ran out of the castle with the magic sword. He found his family and they all went off to Rome.

Back in the castle, the dog began to bark. This woke up the guards. They saw the dead giants.

The King was amazed when he saw the sword was missing. He wondered who had killed the giants.

"We must search every land for the brave knight who has killed the wicked giants," cried the princess. "I shall marry him."

So the King's men built an inn where travellers could stay. A sign above the door said: ANYONE WHO TELLS THE STORY OF HIS LIFE MAY STAY HERE FREE.

Niels and his family walked on towards Rome. Soon they came to the Alps. The path was too steep and their feet were cold. They turned round to go home.

On the way back, they came to the King's new inn. Each one of them told his story. At first Niels was shy. He did not want to say who he was.

Then Niels showed them the sword. "Hoorah!" shouted all the King's men. "This must be the giant killer. Fetch the King and the princess."

The sword was put back on the wall. Niels and the princess were married. From that day onwards, only friendly giants came to visit the King.

Spot the Giant differences

Here are pictures of Giant Glumwit, Mrs Glumwit and their two children. But the two pictures are not quite the same. Can you spot the 20 differences.

King Frederick's Army

This is a true story about King Frederick of Prussia. He wanted giant guardsmen in his army to frighten away all the soldiers of his enemies.

The King sent messengers all over the world for giants. But they were too big and clumsy to fight. They ran away when the enemy charged them.

The Empress of Austria's Party

Long ago the Empress of Austria invited all the giants and dwarfs to a party. Everyone was worried that the giants would frighten the dwarfs.

But the dwarfs tickled and pinched the giants, stole their food and pulled their hair. The giants began to cry and begged to go home again.

Some famous Giants

Tom Hickerthrift was the hero giant of Cambridge. He was so big and strong that he fought with an axle and a cartwheel.

Tom Hickerthrift

Sand Giants

Sand giants sometimes appeared to frighten travellers in the desert.

Paul Bunyan

Paul Bunyan was the monster ma
of the Wild West.

Jordan

Jordan, the Swiss Giant, used to play tricks on mountain climbers in the Alps.

Atlas

Atlas was punished for fighting the Greek god Zeus. He was made to hold up the earth.

Giant Trolls

Giant Trolls lived in caves in the mountains of Norway. They sniffed out children with their long noses.

A Giant Problem

The giant has asked the witch to help him solve this problem. See if you can work it out too. If you cannot the answer is upside down in the middle of the page.

The giant wants to take his dog, his hen and a sack of corn across the river. But his boat is only big enough for himself and either his dog or his hen or the sack of corn.

5. Next he takes the sack of corn across.
6. Then he goes back alone.
7. Finally he brings the hen back.
8. Now they are all safely across.

he takes the dog across first,
e hen will eat the corn.
he takes the corn across first,
e dog will eat the hen.
'hat does the witch tell him to do?

Answer
1. First he takes the hen across.
2. Then he goes back alone.
3. Next he takes the dog across.
4. Then he takes the hen back again.

Witches and Imps

Long ago, people thought witches were horrid old women who wore black clothes. They were afraid that witches would put bad spells on them.

But there were kind witches too, who only made good spells. When a bad witch put a spell on people, they asked a kind witch to take it off.

When one witch wanted to visit a witch friend in the next village, she flew there on her broom stick.

There were also some men witches. They were called warlocks and sometimes flew around on pitchforks.

Each witch had a special helper called an imp. Imps carried out the witch's orders and visited the houses of her enemies to bewitch them.

Many witches also had a black cat a white mouse, a big black raven, a toad, a lizard or an elf to help them with their bad spells.

Each witch made spells by boiling up herbs and other things in a cauldron. Spells only worked if the mixture was stirred anti-clockwise.

Sometimes a witch's spell was so strong that even a white witch could not take it off. Then a priest had to come to drive it out.

The Witches of Canewdon

The village of Canewdon has a very old church. Long ago, the people believed that nine witches who lived in the village kept the church safe.

Canewdon witches did not fly on broom-sticks like other witches. They flew on gates. One day a witch flew over the river to the next village.

She wanted to steal their church bell. She landed on the church roof and lifted it off its hook.

The bell was too heavy to take home on her gate. She ran down the hill with it towards the river.

The people chased her. But she was too quick. She put the bell in a tub, and began to row away.

But when she was half way across, there was a terrible storm. She cried out for help.

No one could help her. The tub turned over. The bell sank and so did the old witch of Canewdon.

Even now, people sometimes say they can hear the old witch ringing her bell at the bottom of the river.

The Witch who lost her Broom stick

One morning, a jolly witch received an invitation to go to a witch's party that afternoon.

She went to get her broom stick to fly to the party. She looked everywhere but she could not find it.

"I'll turn someone into a horse with my magic halter," she said. "Then I can ride to the party."

First she met a man and his wife walking along the road. The man was in front. His wife walked behind, carrying all the heavy luggage.

When the man had passed by, the witch jumped out from behind a tree. Before the wife could cry out, the witch threw the halter over her head.

As soon as the halter touched her, the wife turned into a horse. Then the witch jumped on to the horse's back and galloped away.

The man turned round but his wife had disappeared. He could only see his luggage lying on the ground under a tree.

He looked everywhere for his wife. But he could not find her. Crossly he picked up the luggage and went on his journey alone.

Soon the horse began to limp. When they came to the next village, the witch asked the blacksmith to fit new horseshoes on the horse.

At last, the witch reached the party. All the other witches laughed at her. "What a funny horse!" they cried. "Haven't you got a broom stick?"

Then they all played games and danced round the fire. They made up lots of new spells and told stories about all the trouble they had caused.

When the party was over, all the other witches climbed on their broom sticks and flew home. The jolly witch set off for home on her horse.

Just outside her house, she met the same man again. As she did not need the horse any more, she asked him if he would like to buy it.

The poor man was very tired from carrying all the luggage, so he was delighted to buy the horse. Of course he did not know who it really was.

When he got back to his cottage, the man led the horse into a stable. He took off the saddle. Then he started to take off the magic halter.

As soon as the halter was off, the witch's spell was broken. The horse turned back into his wife.

But one part did not change. She still had horse shoes on her hands and feet.

It took a long time for them to wear off. The man had to carry all the luggage until they did.

The Two Silly Witches

A family of witches once lived
in a cottage at the bottom of a hill.
The chief witch was old and grumpy.

The other two were young and silly.
They forgot to say their spells,
and did not even wear black cloaks.

One day they were even more silly
than usual. They dropped the cauldron
and it broke into two big pieces.

The old witch was very angry.
She set off at once on her broom
stick to buy another cauldron.

When she had gone, the two young witches wondered what to do all day. "Let's make it rain!" one of them said. "That will stop everyone having fun."

They ran to the shelf where the chief witch kept her book of spells. "This one looks easy!" one witch said. "Spell 21. HOW TO MAKE RAIN."

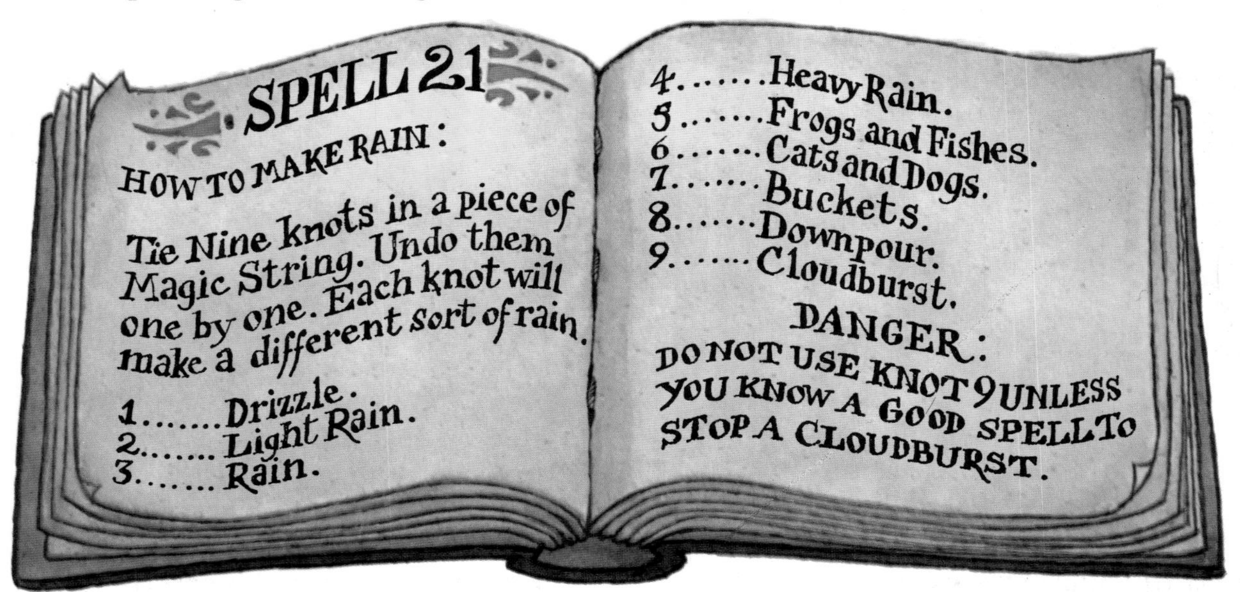

SPELL 21
HOW TO MAKE RAIN:
Tie Nine knots in a piece of Magic String. Undo them one by one. Each knot will make a different sort of rain.
1....... Drizzle.
2....... Light Rain.
3....... Rain.
4....... Heavy Rain.
5....... Frogs and Fishes.
6....... Cats and Dogs.
7....... Buckets.
8....... Downpour.
9....... Cloudburst.
DANGER:
DO NOT USE KNOT 9 UNLESS YOU KNOW A GOOD SPELL TO STOP A CLOUDBURST.

But they did not notice the warning at the end of the spell.

They rushed off to look in the cupboard for a piece of magic string.

They tied nine knots in the string. Then one of the witches quickly untied the first knot.

The other one ran outside to see what was happening. "It really works," she said. "It's drizzling."

"Now let's try some heavy rain," she said. "That should be fun." So they untied the fourth knot.

The fourth knot worked even better. The rain came pouring down until it made big puddles.

"How about a cloud burst?" said the first witch. And she began to undo the last knot in the string.

They went outside to watch. It began to rain so hard their hats and coats were soon wet through.

They ran back into the cottage to find out how to stop the cloud burst. They looked in the book of spells. Then they saw the warning.

"Oh no!" they cried. "What shall we do? It's going to rain for ever." The water rose higher and higher. Soon it was so deep they had to swim.

Then the chief witch flew back with the new cauldron. And she was even crosser than before. The cottage was in the middle of a lake.

But it was only raining on the witches' cottage. Soon the lake covered the roof and the silly witches were never seen again.

The Black Witch and the White Wizard

Early one morning a farmer and his wife set out to work in the fields. Their daughter Jane went too. She carried the picnic lunch.

By the middle of the day, they were all hot and tired. Jane ran to the barn where she had hidden the basket to keep their picnic cool.

When Jane peeped into the barn, she saw an old witch asleep in the hay. The basket was empty. The witch had eaten all the food and drunk the beer.

"You have eaten all our food!" the little girl cried. She pointed at the basket and the empty beer bottle. "You nasty old woman."

'I'll make you sorry!'' the witch said. Then she cast a spell on Jane. 'Maxi-baxi-jollybee-hogg, get down on the ground and bark like a dog.''

Jane ran back to her father and mother. She could not tell them what had happened. She could only bark. And the witch ran off, cackling.

'Come back!'' shouted the farmer. 'What have you done to my daughter?'' But the witch just laughed as she flew away on her broom stick.

The farmer and his wife took Jane back home. Everyone came to look at her. But no one knew how to break the witch's spell.

So they took Jane to see the old white wizard who lived in the cottage on top of the hill. He had an owl and a bat, two cats and a family of mice.

Jane knelt on the floor and barked. "Oh dear!" said the wizard. "What a terrible thing to happen. I wonder which witch has cast this spell?"

"Swashamazoosh!" he cried, looking into his crystal ball. "Show me who has cast the spell on the girl."
The witch's face appeared in the ball.

The wizard began to make a magic brew to break the witch's spell.
He mixed up toadstools, horseshoe nails, mustard and red berries.

When the brew was ready, he heated it over a candle. Then he looked in the crystal ball again. The witch stuck out her tongue. She was not afraid.

The wizard cried out "Tongues of fire come out and chase the witch."
The cork flew out of the bottle and the flames shot up the chimney.

The witch's face in the crystal ball changed from a laugh to a worried frown.

Then she turned and ran away as the tongues of fire chased her.

"Stop!" she cried, as they caught her up. "I'll break the spell on the girl."

The spell was broken as soon as the witch spoke. Jane was not a dog any more. She jumped up from the ground and hugged her mother.

They all waved good bye to the wizard. And they never saw the witch again. But after that Jane was very careful where she hid the picnic basket.

The Farmer's Revenge

Farmer Jones had a big brown cow. He milked her in the morning and he milked her in the evening. Every day she gave him five buckets of milk.

But a greedy witch lived in the same village. She did not keep a cow. She just wanted all Farmer Jones' lovely creamy milk for herself.

One day something very strange happened. Farmer Jones milked his cow, just as he always did.

Then he tipped the milk into the big wooden churn. Now it was ready to be made into butter.

But when he looked into the churn, it was not full of milk at all. The milk had disappeared.

Farmer Jones was angry. He wondered if someone was casting a spell to make his milk disappear.

Next day, at milking time, the farmer's wife went into the village to see who was making trouble.

She saw the witch using the village pump. But it was not water coming out. It was milk.

"Poor farmer Jones!" chuckled the witch. "He'll never know I make his milk disappear into the pump."

The farmer's wife ran all the way back to the farm. She told her husband what she had seen.

"I know what we'll do to beat her," the farmer said. Then he went inside and fetched a big box.

At milking time, farmer Jones took the box with him. Even the big brown cow wondered what it was.

When the farmer had finished milking, he poured the milk into the churn as he always did.

Then he opened the box, and tipped lots of white stuff into the churn. It was a soap powder.

The witch began to pump. "Lovely milk," she cried. She was so greedy, she did not notice the funny taste.

The milk started to bubble and froth. The bubbles filled her mouth and stuck to the end of her nose.

Soon the old witch was covered all over with bubbles. She never tried to steal the milk again.

Janek and his Brothers

There was once a witch who could turn herself into a huge, black bird. Every night she flew down and broke the windows of an old village church.

Three brothers lived in the same village. Every night the older ones guarded the church. But every night they fell asleep before the bird came.

One night the third brother, called Janek, hid in a thorn bush to help him stay awake.

When the bird came swooping down, Janek jumped out of the bush and fired his gun at it.

The bird fell down behind a big rock, and Janek ran to tell his brothers what he had done.

But when they looked behind the rock, the bird had disappeared. There was just a deep hole. So they lowered burning sticks to try and see down it.

Janek wanted to explore the hole. So he climbed down and down through the mist and clouds until at last he reached a strange underground land.

Janek was all alone. He ran along a winding path to a castle and climbed the steps. Slowly he pushed open the huge wooden door.

In the first room he met a girl with golden hair. She was so beautiful that Janek asked her to come up to the world above with him.

But the girl said she had been cursed by the bird witch. She could not leave the castle until some brave man killed the witch with the magic sword.

The girl with the golden hair had two sisters. Janek said he would kill the witch to free them all. So they gave him a special drink to make him strong.

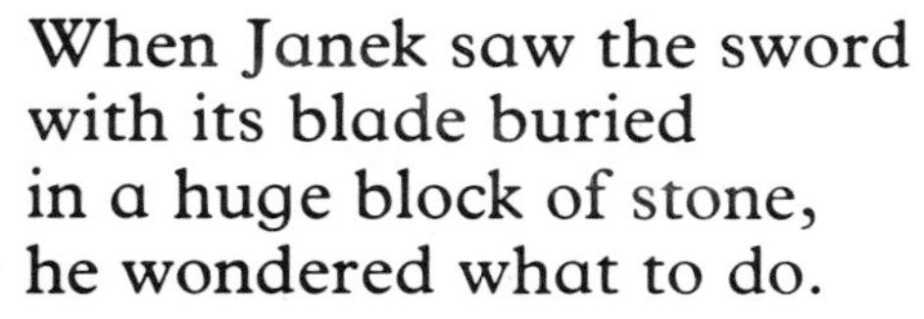

When Janek saw the sword
with its blade buried
in a huge block of stone,
he wondered what to do.

He pulled and pulled.
At first it did not move.
Then slowly it began to
come out of the stone.

At last the sword was
free. Janek waved it
above his head and set
out to find the witch.

Janek waited outside the castle.
Soon the bird came swooping down.
As soon as its feet touched the ground,
it turned back into the witch.

When the witch saw Janek, she leapt
forward to attack him. But Janek was
too quick. He killed her with one
blow from the magic sword.

Janek took the three sisters to the place where he had climbed down the rope. He tied it round them and called to his brothers to pull them up.

Up at the top of the deep hole, Janek's brothers began to pull. At last the three beautiful sisters arrived safely in the world above.

Then Janek ran back to the castle and collected all the treasure. He tied the treasure chest to the rope and called up to his brothers again.

The brothers pulled up the rope. They were delighted when they saw the big chest. Now they had three beautiful sisters and all the treasure.

But Janek was worried. He wondered if his brothers would pull him up safely too.

Janek tied the rope to a big stone. Then he called to his brothers that he was ready to be pulled up.

But when the stone was half way up, his brothers let go of the rope. The stone came crashing down.

Janek was very unhappy. He knew his brothers tried to kill him. There was no other way out. So he wandered round the underground world.

One day, after many months, he met a magician. "If you will guard my children in the apple tree," said the magician, "I will help you escape."

Janek hid in the tree with the babies. Soon a huge serpent attacked them. After a long, terrible fight, Janek killed it with the magic sword.

The old magician was happy when he saw his babies had been saved. "Climb on my back," he said to Janek. "I will take you to the world above."

First the magician said a magic spell. Then, while Janek held on round his neck, he shot up through the clouds and mist, out of the deep hole.

Janek was so pleased to be back, he ran all the way to his brothers' house. He burst open the door.

His brothers and the beautiful sisters were amazed to see him again. They thought that he must be dead.

At first Janek's brothers were frightened and tried to run away. Then they were sorry for what they had tried to do to him.

But Janek was so pleased to be home, he forgave them. They all shared the treasure and each brother married one of the beautiful sisters.

Witches at Night

The best time for witches to go flying was when the moon was full. This was because of the magic power of moonlight.

Witches lived in the first house of the village.

Witches sometimes danced round their chief witch to cast a spell.

The chief witch had a white mouse and a black cat to help her.

People thought ringing church bells would frighten witches.

Witches sometimes rested on roof tops or flew down the chimney.

Horseshoes kept away witches.

Witches stirred egg shells in a cauldron. People believed that ships at sea would sink when the egg shells sank.

Old ladies who looked like witches were ducked and were often killed.

Answer to problem on page 32

This is the way the giant went to get the dragon's treasure.

First published in 1979 by
Usborne Publishing Ltd,
20 Garrick Street,
London WC2 9BJ, England.

Printed in Belgium.